For my bright,
beautiful niece Rosie
~ NE

For Rowan
& Magnus
~ HT

The Forest Stewardship Council® (FSC®) is an international, non-governmental organisation dedicated to promoting responsible management of the world's forests. FSC operates a system of forest certification and product labelling that allows consumers to identify wood and wood-based products from well-managed forests and other controlled sources.

For more information about the FSC, please visit their website at www.fsc.org

CATERPILLAR BOOKS
An imprint of the Little Tiger Group
www.littletiger.co.uk
1 Coda Studios, 189 Munster Road, London SW6 6AW
First published in Great Britain 2021
Text by Nicola Edwards • Text copyright © Caterpillar Books Ltd 2021
Illustrations copyright © Hannah Tolson 2021
A CIP catalogue record for this book is available from the British Library
All rights reserved • Printed in China
ISBN: 978-1-83891-177-5 • CPB/1600/1644/0121
1 3 5 7 9 10 8 6 4 2

Look to the Skies

The yearly migration of the majestic monarch
butterfly across North America and back again
is a truly breathtaking, unique phenomenon.

This beautiful flight of bright, beating
wings unites young and old, rich and poor,
city-dwellers and country-folk, as people pause their
daily hustle and bustle and look up to see a
sky parade like no other on Earth.

We stop what we're doing and **gaze** at the **skies**,
We stand open-mouthed with the widest of eyes.

For three thousand miles they will follow the sun,
The **magical sky parade** now has begun!

In the shade of the forest, one warm summer's day,
We swing and we splash and we laugh and we play.

Then past the tall peaks, on the pine-scented breeze,
They come, so **majestic**. Wings **beat** through the trees.

As **green** boughs blush **golden**, the air starts to cool,
We're dressed in new clothes, **fresh** and **ready** for school.

A bright orange **flash** makes us freeze in the street:
The **monarchs** are here! What a **glorious** treat!

Our city is **bustling, busy** and **bright,**
With so much to see, whether morning or night.

But when they appear, our jaws drop, we stop dead.
They **flitter** and **flutter** like **jewels** overhead.

The **harvest** is done now
with all it can yield;
The **sweet** smell of cornbread
drifts over the **field**.

And then in the **hush** of the dusk come their **wings**.
Oh, **nature** is full of such **wonderful things!**

With days growing darker and winter ahead,
We kick **piles of leaves**, crispy brown, gold and red.

FOR SALE

Bright pumpkins are carved, they will soon come alive,
And it's time for the **orange parade** to arrive!

We love to play out in the white glistening **snow**,
But once the cold threatens, the **monarchs** must go.

They need the relief that the warmer south brings,
They all yearn to feel the **sun's rays** on their **wings**.

On our **wide rolling plains**, horses take in the view,
Gazing up at the **heavenly** purple, pink, blue.

When we look up high
and see **bright wings** unfurled,
That's when we feel everything's
right with the **world**.

Our city's a **riot of colour** splashed loud,
It's **beautiful**, whether in sunshine or cloud.

But we're still in awe of the **monarch sky show**,
They've come a **long way**, not much further to go.

In ancient fir forests are towering trees,
No branches or boughs are as welcome as these.

The butterflies hustle and jostle for space,
A butterfly blanket, as each takes its place.

Three thousand miles is a valiant quest.
Now beneath the **blue skies**, our travellers **rest**.

They taught us all to look up to the skies,
There's **magic** around us. Just open your **eyes**.

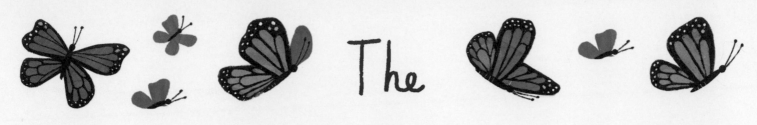

The MONARCH BUTTERFLY

These butterflies are seeking warmer weather as they are not able to cope with frosty temperatures. They find their perfect microclimate in Mexico's ancient oyamel fir forests. These forests only exist at altitudes over 2,400m (7,900ft) and are sadly endangered, with only 2% of the original forests remaining.

It can take as many as five generations of monarchs, breeding en-route, to complete the journey from the north to the south and back again. It's believed that the butterflies have a kind of inbuilt compass that lets them sense the direction they need to travel, using the Earth's magnetic field.

Conservation of oyamel forests is essential to the future of monarchs as is the survival of the milkweed wildflower, which is the only thing monarch caterpillars eat. We need more people to grow milkweed for monarch butterflies to eat while they travel on their long journey.

Monarchs are
found as far north as
southern Canada, on both
sides of the Rocky Mountains.
The western monarchs will travel
to central and southern California
to spend the winter while those
that live east of the Rocky
Mountains will migrate as
far south as Mexico.